New Scooter for Scott

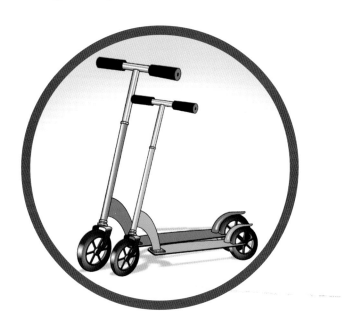

written by Jay Dale

illustrated by Peggy Mozley

"Oh, dear," said Mum.

"We don't have Scott's red scooter.

He will have to stay here with me."

"No, thanks," said Scott.
"I don't want to stay with you.
I want to ride a scooter.
I want to go to the playground
with Dad and Lin."

"You can still come with us," smiled Dad.

"We will ride our scooters and you can walk."

"No, thanks," said Scott.

"I don't want to walk.

I want to ride a scooter."

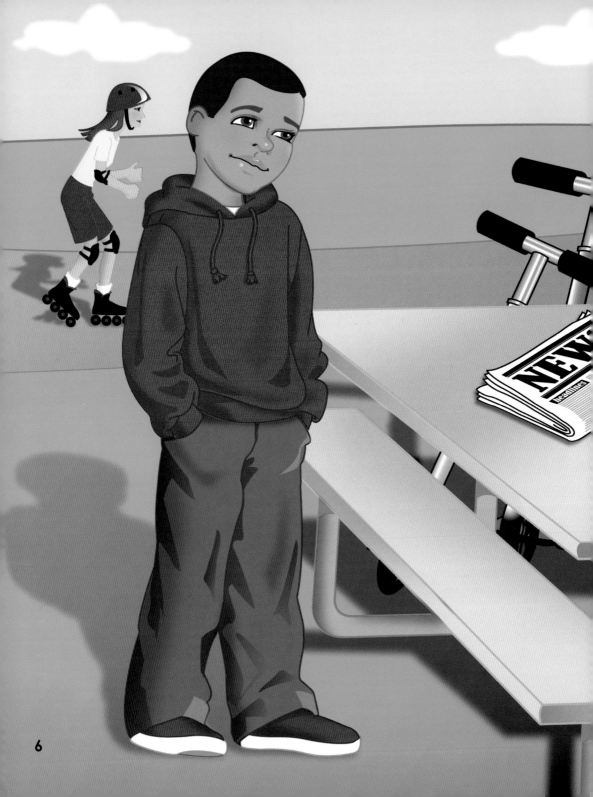

"Oh, dear," said Mum.

"We have two scooters.

We have a big scooter for Dad

and a little scooter for Lin.

We don't have three scooters."

Scott looked sad.

He sat down at the table.

"I want to ride a scooter," he said.

"I want to go to the playground

with Dad and Lin."

Dad looked at Scott.

Then he started to smile.

"Come with me," he said.

"You **can** ride a scooter."

Scott and Dad went onto the path.
Dad took his big blue scooter.

"Now," said Dad.

"Put your right foot here.

Then put your left foot next to it."

Scott put his right foot
on the scooter.
Then he put his left foot next to it.

"Are you ready?" asked Dad.

"Yes!" smiled Scott.
"I'm ready.
Let's go!"

And with that, Scott and Dad **_zoomed_** along the path.

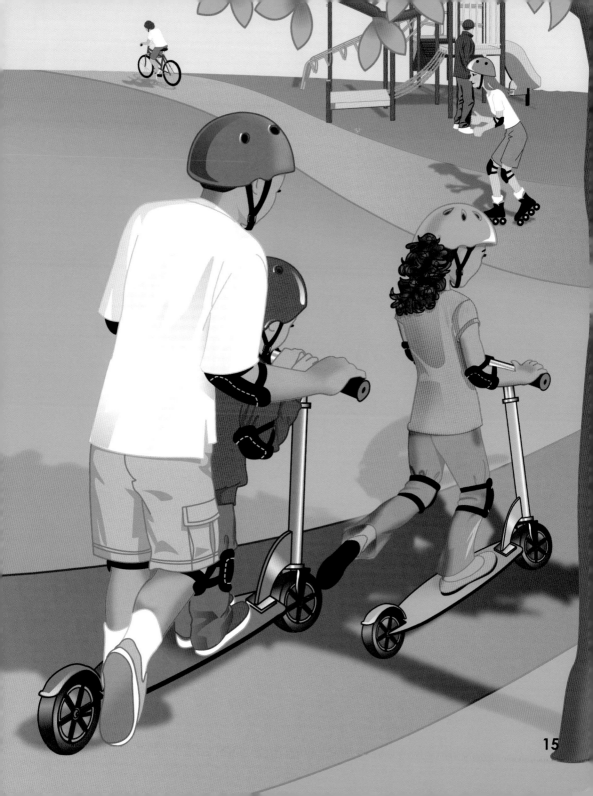

"Yippee!" shouted Scott.

"Look at me!

I **can** ride a scooter, too!"